To: _____

From: _____

My Grandparents are the greatest.
When they go travelling they see
the coolest things!

This year they visited Toronto in Canada.

DID YOU KNOW?

- Toronto is the largest city in Canada and the fourth largest in North America next to Mexico City, Los Angeles and New York City. It is the capital of the province of Ontario.
- Initially Toronto was a French fur trading post (Fort Rouillé). It was then named the Town of York by the British in 1793, and finally in 1834 was officially named Toronto.
- The earliest name for Toronto comes from a Mohawk First Nations word *tkaronto,* which means "where there are trees standing in the water".

They went on the *Maid of the Mist* river boat to the bottom of Niagara Falls.

DID YOU KNOW?
- Over 150 million litres of water flow over the falls every minute!
- Niagara Falls is split into three main falls: The Canadian Horseshoe Falls, Bridal Veil Falls and the American Falls.
- The falls sit on the Niagara River, which flows from four Great Lakes and now form the border between Ontario and the state of New York.
- Ocean going ships can bypass the falls via the Welland Canal and thereby travel from Chicago on Lake Michigan, down the St Lawrence Seaway all the way through to the Atlantic Ocean.

They climbed 1776 steps to the top of the giant CN Tower.

DID YOU KNOW?
- The CN Tower is 553 metres high, was built in 1976 by the Canadian National Railway (CN).
- The tower stands at one end of Toronto's main street: Yonge Street. Yonge Street is touted as the longest street in the world (1,896 km), stretching from Lake Ontario to Lake Simcoe in the upper Great Lakes region of the province.
- Toronto has over 2,000 high-rises over 30 metres - second only to New York City in all of North America.

From the glass floors on top you can see as far as the United States of America.

There were all kinds of foods from many different cultures.

DID YOU KNOW?
- Over half of the Greater Toronto Area's 6.1 million people were born outside of Canada, and over 140 languages and dialects are spoken by residents.
- In the last 60 years Toronto has been settled by waves of immigrants from Italy, Poland, Portugal, the UK, Greece, Chile, the Caribbean, India, China, Hong Kong and more. The United Nations has named Toronto as one of the most culturally diverse cities in the world.
- Toronto has over 8,000 restaurants serving food from over 80 different cultures.

They saw black bears and busy beavers.

DID YOU KNOW?
- Algonquin Park is the oldest and largest provincial park in Ontario and one of over 100 in the province. It covers 7,500 square kilometres and hosts over 2,400 lakes.
- The beaver is a large herbivorous rodent known for its powerful buck teeth, large flat tail and webbed hind feet. The beaver is considered the national animal of Canada.
- Canada is home to three species of bears: The American black bear, the polar bear and the brown bear. Black bears, usually nocturnal and solitary creatures, are meat eaters, but also eat berries, fruit, grubs, eggs and roots.

Toronto and Algonquin Provincial Park have amazing and funny-looking wildlife.

They saw lots and lots and lots...

of squirrels!

DID YOU KNOW?
- There are over 250 species of squirrel, with the Eastern Tree Gray Squirrel (often black in colour) being the most common in Toronto. Chipmunks, prairie dogs and groundhogs are members of the squirrel rodent family.
- The squirrel eats nuts, acorns, seeds, buds, fruit and birds' eggs. They store the food in small burrows in the ground or in their nests (dreys) during the summer to last them for the winter.
- In Toronto's suburbs, it is not uncommon to see other wild animals such as skunks, raccoons, coyote, fox, rabbits and deer search for food.

They went to a professional ice hockey game in a huge arena.

DID YOU KNOW?
- Ice hockey originated in Canada and it is the country's official winter sport.
- Toronto is home to the Canadian Hockey Hall of Fame.
- Lacrosse is the official summer sport and dates back to First Nations people – it is a game of passing and catching a ball using sticks with a nested pouch at one end.
- Canadians also invented the game of basketball, tobogganing, five pin bowling, jet-skiing and synchronized swimming.

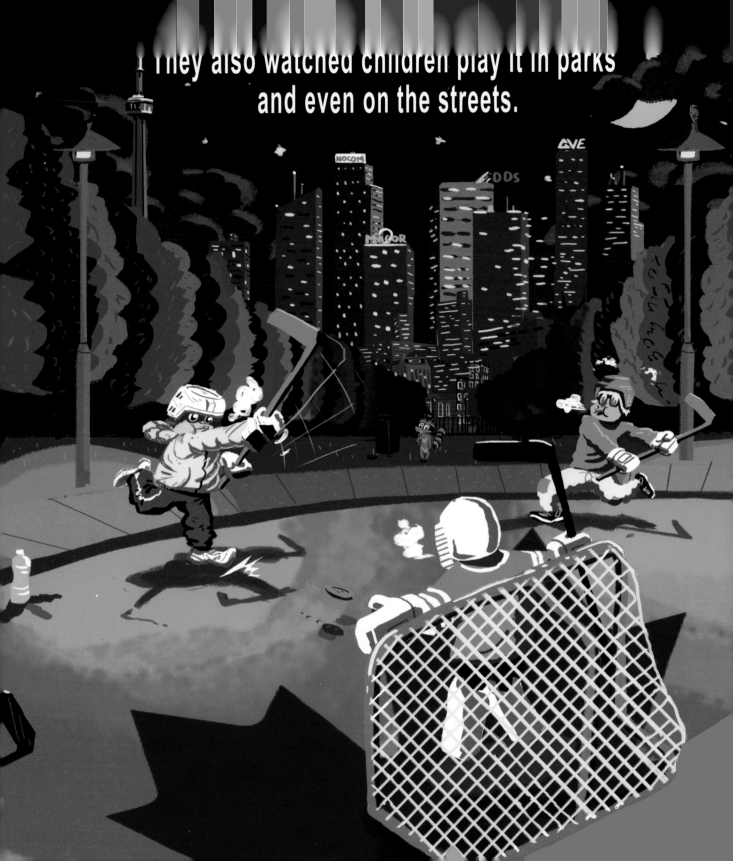

They also watched children play it in parks and even on the streets.

They went out for breakfast and had pancakes, waffles and French toast topped with lots of maple syrup.

DID YOU KNOW?

- The sugar maple is a hardwood deciduous tree that is tapped for sap in the spring each year taking 30-50 litres of sap to make one litre of maple syrup.
- Canada produces over 80% of the world's maple syrup.
- The flow of sap that is trapped in buckets is called a run, and the boiling down of the collected sap to produce maple syrup is undertaken in a sugarhouse or "sugar shack".
- The maple tree is Canada's national tree, and the maple leaf appears at the centre of its flag and coat of arms.

Canada is famous for its maple trees.

But do you know the most interesting thing?
Even though Grandma and Grandpa saw lots of cool things...

They said they still missed me!

Grandma and Grandpa's diary pages:

Date of arrival:_____

Date of departure:_____

Grandma's favourite day/activity:_____
_____
_____
_____

Grandpa's favourite day/activity:_____
_____
_____
_____

Favourite food:_____

Favourite drink:_____

Most interesting thing:_____
_____
_____
_____
_____

奶奶爷爷的多伦多探险记

Translated by 陈美凤

我的奶奶爷爷最了不起了。当他们去旅游时，总是能见识到最有趣的事物。
今年他们去了加拿大的多伦多。

他们坐了「雾中少女号」到尼加拉瀑布底下。
瀑布是如此雄伟，令人印象深刻，激起云朵般的喷雾，声震如雷。

他们爬了1776个阶梯，到巨型CN塔的最高层。
从顶层的玻璃地板可以看到远处的美国。

他们搭乘电车环游了市区。
有好多不同文化的各种食品。

他们看到了黑熊与忙碌的海狸。
多伦多和阿冈昆省立公园里有令人称奇和长像怪异的野生动物。

他们看到了很多，很多，很多......松鼠！

他们去一个大溜冰场看了一场专业的冰球比赛。
也看到孩子们在公园里练习，连在街道上都在玩。

他们出去吃早餐，有煎饼、松饼和法式吐司，淋上了大量的枫糖浆。
加拿大是以枫树出名的。

可是，你知道最有意思的是什麽吗？尽管我奶奶爷爷在旅途中看了好多有趣的事情……
但是，他们说一路上仍然想念着我！

おじいちゃんとおばあちゃんのトロント大冒険
Translated by Takane Kirkman

ぼくのおじいちゃんとおばあちゃんはサイコーさ。旅行（りょこう）に行（い）って
いろんなものを見（み）て来（く）るんだ。
今年（ことし）は、カナダのトロントへ行ったんだよ。

二人（ふたり）は「霧の乙女号（きりのおとめごう）」に乗（の）って
ナイアガラの滝（たき）を見に行った。
ナイアガラの滝はとにかく大（おお）きくて、雲（くも）のような水（みず）しぶきをあげて、
雷（かみなり）のような音（おと）をたてながら落（お）ちて来（く）るんだって。

CNタワーでは、頂上（ちょうじょう）まで1776段（だん）もの階段（かいだん）をのぼった。
頂上の展望台（てんぼうだい）からは、遠く（とおく）にアメリカも見えるんだって。

街（まち）では路面電車（ろめんでんしゃ）に乗って、あちこちへ行った。
そこでは世界（せかい）のいろいろな食べ物（たべもの）が売（う）られていたって。

黒（くろ）くまやはたらき者（もの）のビーバーにも会（あ）ったんだって。
トロントやアルゴンキン州立公園（しゅうりつこうえん）には、面白い（おもしろい）
生き物（いきもの）がたくさんいるんだ。

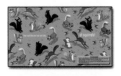

それからリス、どこへ行ってもリスがいっぱい！

プロのアイスホッケーを見るために大きなアリーナへ行った。
カナダの子供（こども）たちは、公園（こうえん）や通り（とおり）でホッケーをして
遊ぶ（あそぶ）んだって。

朝（あさ）ごはんは、メープルシロップたっぷりのパンケーキ、ワッフル、フレンチトースト。
メープルシロップは、カナダの名物（めいぶつ）なんだ。

でも、ぼくにとって一番（いちばん）うれしかったことはなんだと思う（おもう）。
おじいちゃんとおばあちゃんはいろんなものを見てきたけど、
ぼくに会（あ）えないのが、とってもさびしかったんだって！

奶奶爺爺的多倫多探險記

Translated by 陳美夙

我的奶奶爺爺最了不起了。當他們去旅遊時，總是能見識到最有趣的事物。
今年他們去了加拿大的多倫多。

他們坐了「霧中少女號」到尼加拉瀑布底下。
瀑布是如此雄偉，令人印象深刻，激起雲朵般的噴霧，聲震如雷。

他們爬了1776個階梯，到巨型CN塔的最高層。
從頂層的玻璃地板可以看到遠處的美國。

他們搭乘電車環遊了市區。
有好多不同文化的各種食品。

他們看到了黑熊與忙碌的海狸。
多倫多和阿岡昆省立公園裡有令人稱奇和長像怪異的野生動物。

他們看到了很多，很多，很多......松鼠！

他們去一個大溜冰場看了一場專業的冰球比賽。
也看到孩子們在公園裡練習，連在街道上都在玩。

他們出去吃早餐，有煎餅、鬆餅和法式吐司，淋上了大量的楓糖漿。
加拿大是以楓樹出名的。

可是，你知道最有意思的是什麼嗎？儘管我奶奶爺爺在旅途中看了好多有趣的事情⋯⋯
但是，他們說一路上仍然想念著我！

A Aventura da vovó e do vovô em Toronto

Traduzido por: Mariana Ciocca Alves Passos

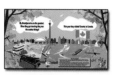

A minha vovó e o meu vovô são os melhores. Quando eles viajam eles vêem as coisas mais legais!
Esse ano, eles foram para Toronto, no Canadá.

Eles passearam de barco "Maid of the Mist" até a base das Cataratas do Niágara.
As Cataratas são tão grandes e impressionantes que elas produzem nuvens de vapor e um barulho de trovão.

Eles subiram 1776 degraus até o topo da gigante Torre CN.
Do chão de vidro, lá no topo, podemos ver até os Estados Unidos da América.

Eles andaram de bonde por toda a cidade.
Havia todos os tipos de comidas de muitas culturas diferentes.

Eles viram ursos negros e castores ocupados.
O *Toronto and Algonquin Provincial Park* tem uma vida selvagem maravilhosa e engraçada.

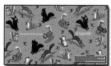

Eles viram muitos e muitos e muitos... esquilos!

Eles foram a um jogo profissional de hóquei no gelo, em um estádio enorme.
Eles também viram crianças jogando hóquei em parques e até nas ruas.

Eles saíram pra tomar café da manhã e comeram panquecas, waffles e torradas francesas com muito xarope de bordo (maple syrup).
O Canadá é famoso pelas suas árvores de Acer (maple trees).

Mas sabe o que é mais interessante?
Mesmo depois da vovó e do vovô verem muitas coisas legais...
Eles disseram que sentiram saudades de mim!

Oma & Opa's Abenteuer in Toronto.

Translated by Hayley Johns & Roland Seydell

Meine Oma und Opa sind die Besten. Wenn sie reisen, sehen sie die tollsten Sachen. Dieses Jahr besuchten sie Toronto in Kanada.

Sie fuhren mit dem Flussdampfer „Maid of the Mist" an den Grund der Niagara Fälle. Die Fälle sind groß und eindrucksvoll. Sie produzieren Gischtwolken und hören sich an wie brüllender Donner.

Sie bestiegen die 1776 Treppenstufen bis zur Spitze des gigantischen CN Turmes. Von der aussichtsplattform kann man bis in die USA sehen.

Sie fuhren mit der Strassenbahn überall in der Stadt herum. Dort gab es gab allerlei Arten von Speisen aus vielen vershiedenen Ländern.

Sie sahen Schwarzbären und fleißige Biber. In Toronto und Algonquin Provincial Park gibt es erstaunliche und lustig aussehende Tiere.

Sie sahen viele, viele, viele Eichhörnchen!

Sie gingen zu einem Profi-Eishockeyspiel in einem riesigen Stadion. Sie beobachteten auch kinder, die im park oder sogar auf ihren strassen hockey spielten.

Sie gingen zum Frühstücken nach draußen und aßen Pfannkuchen, Waffeln und Toast mit ganz viel Ahornsirup darauf. Kanada ist berühmt für seine Ahornbäume.

Aber weisst du, was das Interessanteste ist? Obwohl Oma und Opa so viele tolle Dinge erlebt haben... Sie haben mich trotzdem vermisst!

Les aventures de Grand-père et Grand-mère à Toronto

Translated by Camille Dumas

Mon grand-père et ma grand-mère sont géniaux.
Quand ils voyagent, ils voient des choses incroyables!
Cette année ils sont allés à Toronto au Canada.

Ils sont allés aux pieds des chutes du Niagara à bord du bateau « Maid of the Mist ».
Les chutes sont si grandes et impressionnantes qu'il en sort des nuages d'embruns dans un grondement tonitruant.

Ils ont monté 1776 marches jusqu'en haut de l'immense Tour CN.
Depuis le dernier étage vitré on peut même voir les Etats Unis d'Amérique.

Ils ont fait le tour de la ville en tramway.
Il y avait de la nourriture de tout plein de pays différents.

Ils ont vu des ours noirs et des castors besogneux.
A Toronto et dans le parc provincial d'Algonquin, les animaux sauvages sont drôlement beaux.

Ils ont vu beaucoup, beaucoup…d'écureuils !

Ils ont assisté à un match de hockey professionnel dans un immense stade.
Ils ont aussi regardé des enfants y jouer dans des parcs et même dans la rue.

Ils ont pris le petit-déjeuner au restaurant et ils ont mangé des pancakes, des gaufres,
et du pain perdu avec plein de sirop d'érable. Le Canada est connu pour ses érables.

Mais tu sais le meilleur dans tout ça ?
Même si Grand-père et Grand-mère ont vu beaucoup de choses incroyables…
Ils ont dit que je leur avais quand même manqué !

La Aventura de la Abuela y el Abuelo en Toronto

Traducido por Miriam de la Puente

Mi Abuela y mi Abuelo son los mejores. ¡Cuando se van de viaje ven las cosas más increibles! Este año fueron a Toronto en Canadá.

Se fueron en el barco "Maid of the Mist"por el río a la parte de abajo de las cataratas del Níagara. Las cataratas son tan grandes e impresionantes que crean nubes de espuma y un estruendoso rugido.

Subieron 1776 escalones hasta la cima de la gigantesca Torre CN.
Desde los pisos de cristal de la parte de arriba se puede ver tan lejos como hasta los Estados Unidos de América.

Se subieron a un tranvia para recorrer toda la ciudad.
Habia todo tipo de comida de diferentes culturas.

Vieron osos negros y castores ocupados.
Toronto y el Parque Provincial de Algonquin tienen una increible y divertida forma para ver la vida silvestre.

Vieron montones y montones y montones de... ardillas!

Fueron a un partido profesional de hockey sobre hielo en un gran estadio.
También vieron niños jugando en los parques e incluso en las calles.

Salieron a desayunar y comieron panqueques, waffles y pan Francés con mucha miel de arce.
Canadá es famoso por sus árboles de arce.

Pero, ¿sabes que es lo más interesante?
Que aunque la Abuela y el Abuelo vieron un montón de cosas increibles...
¡Dijeron que aún así me extrañaron!